Zaner-Bloser

Handwriting

Zaner-Bloser

Senior Consultant
Steve Graham, Ed.D., Currey Ingram Professor of Special Education and Literacy, Vanderbilt University

Occupational Therapy Consultants
Jane Case-Smith, Ed.D., OTR/L, FAOTA, Chair of the Occupational Therapy Division, Ohio State University
Mary Benbow, M.S., OTR, La Jolla, CA
Asha Asher, MA OTR/L, FAOTA, M.Ed. (Special Education), Cincinnati, OH
North Shore Pediatric Therapy

ELL Consultants
Ellen Riojas Clark, Ph.D., Professor of Bicultural-Bilingual Studies, University of Texas at San Antonio
Bertha Pérez, Ed.D., Professor Emeritus of Literacy, University of Texas at San Antonio

Consultant
Debbie Diller, Educational Consultant, Houston, TX

Occupational Therapy Advisory Board
Kathleen A. Benton-Sanchez, M.P.A., OTR/L, Nashville, TN
Sherry Eisenbach, OT/L, Portland, OR
Elizabeth Gerich, OTR/L, Plymouth, MN
Sheila Martins, OTR/L, North Las Vegas, NV
Carol Miller, OTR/L, Marietta, OH
Leslie N. Parker, OTR/L, Huntington, WV
Tricia Shibuya, OTR/L, Las Vegas, NV
Denaysa Sisemore, M.S., OTR/L, Windsor, CO
Cheryl Weaver, CAS, M.S.Ed., OTR/L, Macedon, NY

Reviewers
Amy Bass, National Heritage Academies, Byron Center, MI
Donetta S. Brown, Birmingham City Schools, AL
Kelly Caravelli, Poway Unified School District, San Diego, CA
Michelle Corsi, East Windsor Regional Schools, NJ
Naomi Drewitz, East Windsor Regional Schools, NJ
Shan Glandon, Tulsa, OK
Karen Jackson, School District of Philadelphia, PA
Liz Knowles, Ed.D., 21st Century Curriculum Designs, LLC, Del Ray Beach, FL
Rita Olsen, Chicago Public Schools, IL
Geraldine A. Pappas, Detroit Public Schools, MI
Michael E. Pizzingrillo, Roman Catholic Diocese of Brooklyn, NY
Deborah C. Thomas, Ed.D., Montgomery Public Schools, AL
Ellen Lerch Thomsen, Roanoke County Public Schools, VA
Iefay Williams, School District of Philadelphia, PA

Credits
Art: Mircea Catusanu/Painted Words: 3 (parrot), 16, 18, 20, 22, 26–28, 32, 34, 36, 38, 41, 43; Nathan Jarvis: 3 (cat), 4, 94, 96, 102; Jan Bryan-Hunt/Painted Words: 8, 9, 112–115, 118 (right); Tim Beaumont/Painted Words: 44, 46, 48, 50, 56, 58, 60, 62, 64, 66, 69; Cheryl Mendenhall/Cornell & McCarthy: 53; Gary Krejca/Wilkinson Studios: 72, 86, 87, 104, 105, 108; Bob Masheris/Wilkinson Studios: 74, 76, 78, 80, 81, 88, 89, 92–93, 98–101, 106; John Hovell: 110, 118 (spot art)

Literature: "Seasons Afoot" by Beverly McLoughland, ©1987 Highlights for Children, Inc., Columbus, Ohio. Used by permission of Highlights for Children, Inc.; "City" by Langston Hughes, from *The Collected Poems of Langston Hughes*, by Langston Hughes. © 1994 by The Estate of Langston Hughes, Alfred A. Knopf, a division of Random House, Inc. Published by Random House, Inc. All rights reserved.; "Only My Opinion" from GOOSE GRASS RHYMES by Monica Shannon, copyright 1930 by Doubleday, a division of Random House, Inc. Used by permission of Doubleday, a division of Random House, Inc.; "People" by Charlotte Zolotow, from *All That Sunlight* by Charlotte Zolotow. ©1967 by Charlotte Zolotow. Copyright renewed 1995.
Used by permission of Scott Treimel NY.

Photos: ©Paul Souders/Corbis: Cover; George C. Anderson Photography, Inc.: 5, 10, 11, 23; ©Duane Rieder/Getty Images: 6–7 (background); ©Bloomimage/Corbis: 6 (rollerbladers); ©Jose Luis Pelaez Inc/Getty Images: 6 (snowman); ©Image Source/Getty Images: 7 (feet); ©Radius/SuperStock: 7 (bus); ©iStock-photo.com/AttaBoyLuther: 24–25; ©Don Johnston/Photolibrary; 30–31: ©Blend Images/SuperStock; 55; ©Timothy Hearsum /Getty Images: 71; ©Janine Wiedel Photolibrary/Alamy: 83: ©Ron Niebrugge/Alamy; 90 (cow); ©Brand X Pictures/Jupiterimages: 90–91; ©Cordaiy Photo Library Ltd./CORBIS: 111; ©CEF/Getty Images: 116

ISBN-978-0-7367-6837-5 15 16 17 18 997 20 19 18 17

Zaner-Bloser, Inc.
1-800-421-3018
www.zaner-bloser.com
Printed in the United States of America

Zaner-Bloser

Unit 4 Using What You Have Learned

Your Book

Models and Guidelines

There are writing models in your book. The models are on guidelines. The red arrows and numerals show you how to write each letter.

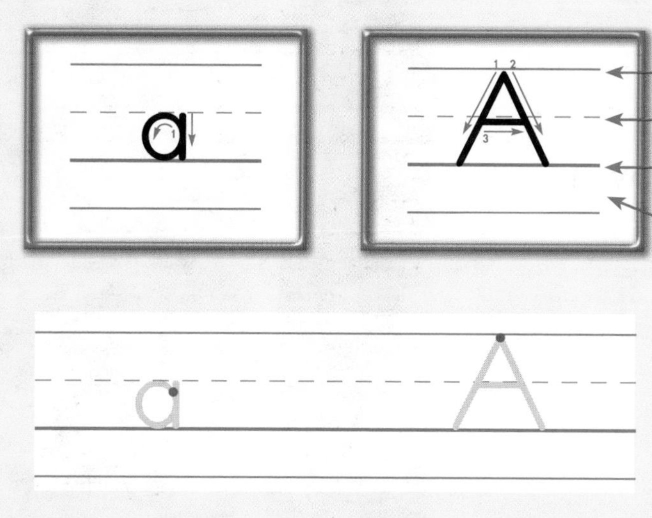

Start at the green dot when you trace and write.

Stop and Check

When you see a **Stop and Check** sign, circle the best letter you wrote on that line.

Circle the best letter on this line.

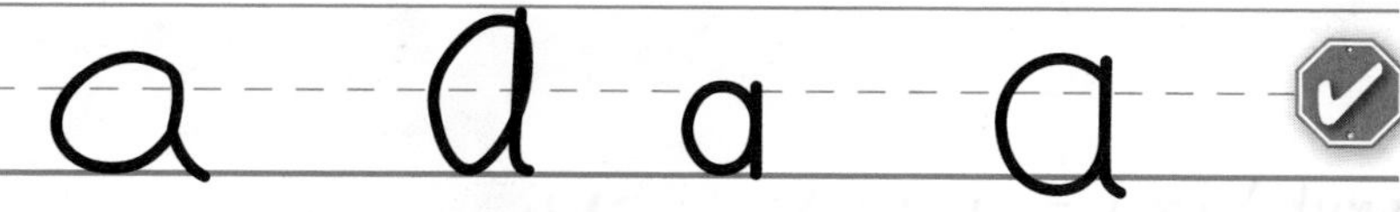

Keys to Legibility

There are four kinds of keys in your book.
The words on the keys are **Shape, Size, Spacing,** and **Slant**.

Good writers think about these things when they write.
The Keys will help you make your writing legible.
Legible means easy to read.

Seasons Afoot

Spring wheels in
On roller skates,
Zooms up and down
The street.

Winter plods in
Heavily
With snow-boots
On its feet.

Summer jumps in
Barefoot,
Kicking water
In the pool.

Autumn squeaks
In brand-new shoes—
Nervously, to
School.

Beverly McLoughland

Unit 1

Getting Started

Pretest

Show What You Can Do

City

In the morning the city
Spreads its wings
Making a song
In stone that sings.

Write the title and the first four lines of the poem.

Write the next four lines here.

If you write with your LEFT hand . . .

Sit like this.
Sit comfortably. Lean forward a little. Keep your feet flat on the floor.

Place the paper like this.

Slant the paper as shown in the picture.

Rest both arms on the desk. Use your right hand to move the paper as you write.

Pull the pencil toward your left elbow when you write.

Hold the pencil like this.

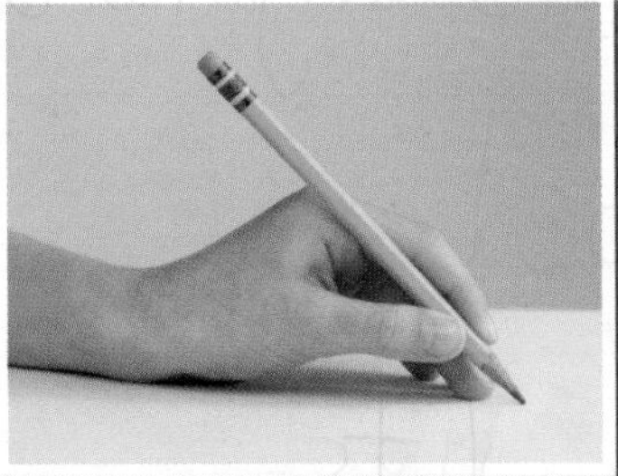

Hold the pencil with your thumb and first two fingers.

Do not squeeze the pencil when you write.

If you write with your **RIGHT** hand . . .

Sit like this.

Sit comfortably. Lean forward a little. Keep your feet flat on the floor.

Place the paper like this.

Place the paper straight in front of you.

Rest both arms on the desk. Use your left hand to move the paper as you write.

Pull the pencil toward the middle of your body when you write.

Hold the pencil like this.

Hold the pencil with your thumb and first two fingers.

Do not squeeze the pencil when you write.

Vertical Lines

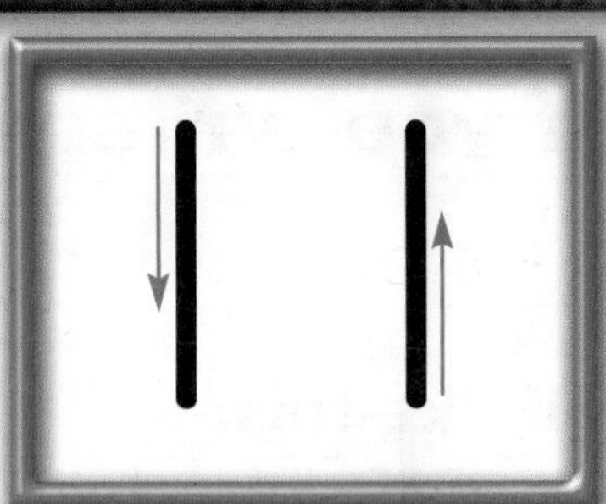

Some letters and numerals have lines that are straight up and down. Trace the straight up and down lines in these letters and numerals.

l b i p h T E L 5 4

Trace and write these letters and numerals that have vertical lines. Start at the green dot.

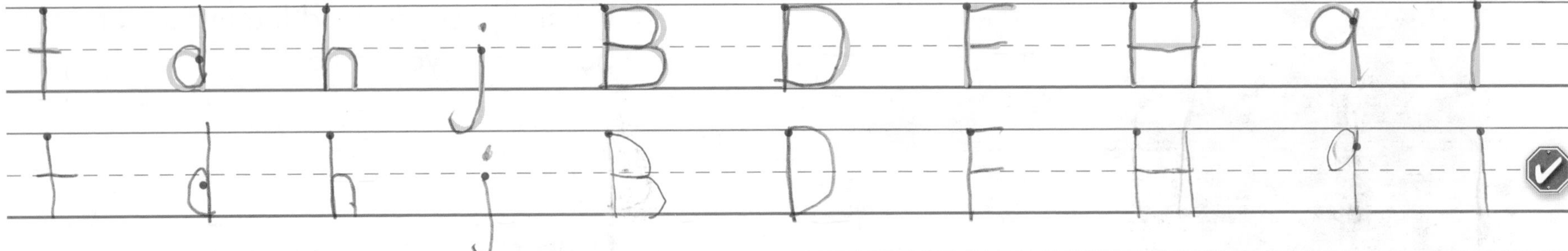

Write the sentence.

Some strokes are vertical lines.

Horizontal Lines

Some letters and numerals have lines that slide right or slide left.
Trace the slide lines in each letter and numeral.

f t e H J G Z 5 2

Trace and write these letters and numerals that have horizontal lines.
Start at the green dot.

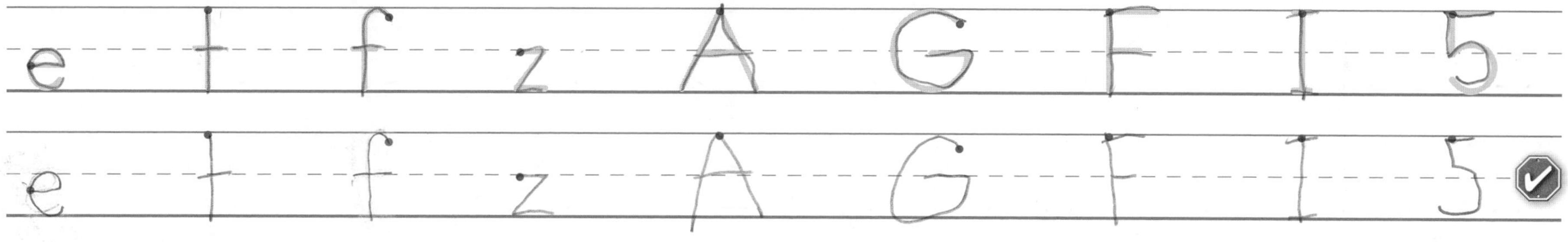

Write the sentence.

Some strokes are horizontal lines.

Circle Lines

Some letters and numerals have forward circle or backward circle lines. Trace the circle or part of the circle in each letter and numeral.

c e g C O b p 2 3

Trace and write these letters and numerals that have circle lines. Start at the green dot.

a d f o C B P 3 8

a d f o C B P 3 8

Write the sentence.

Some strokes are circle lines.

Slant Lines

Some letters and numerals have lines that slant left or slant right.
Trace the slant lines in each letter and numeral.

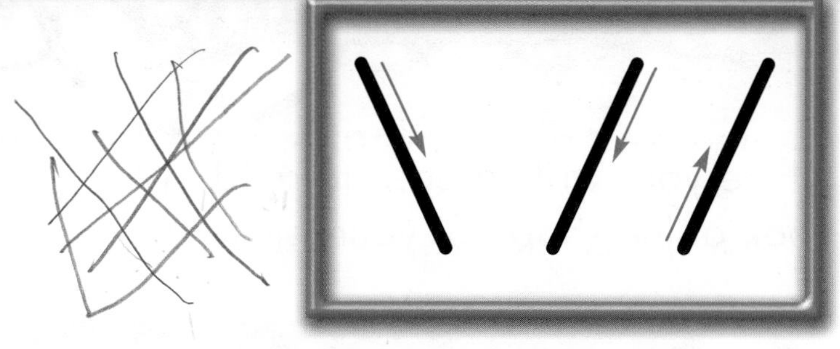

x z k v W Q A X 7

Trace and write these letters and numerals that have slant lines.
Start at the green dot.

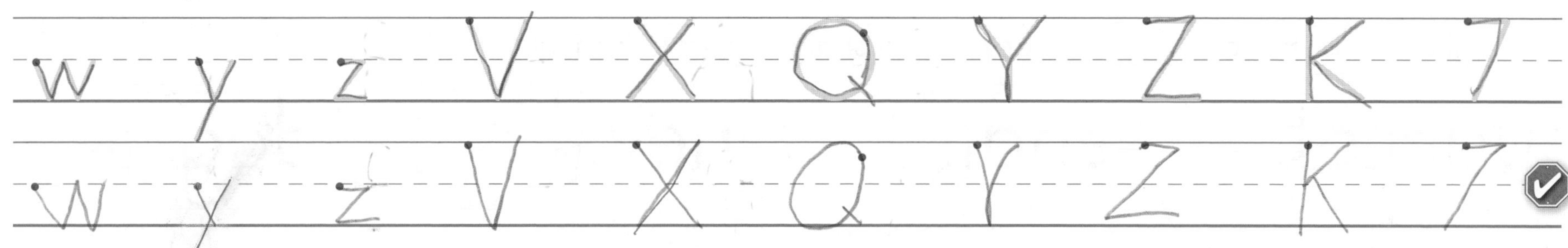

Write the sentence.

Some strokes are slant lines.

Make your writing easy to read.
Look at the shape of your letters.

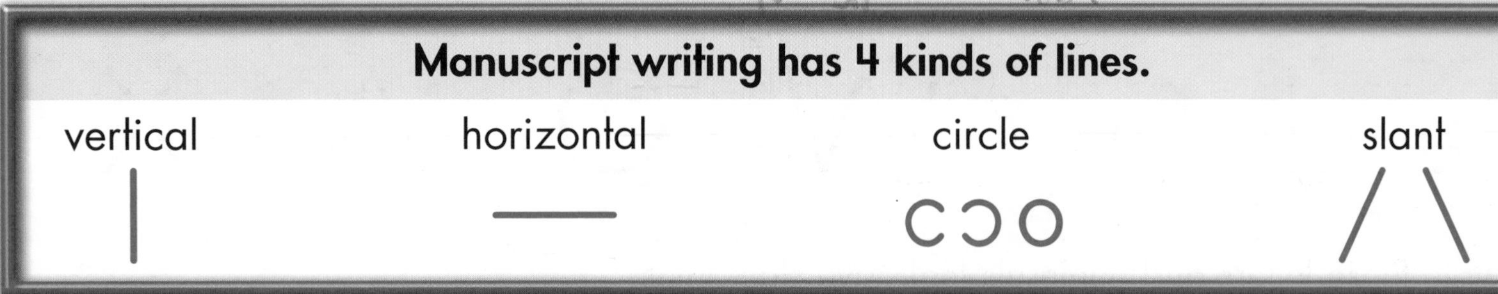

Manuscript writing has 4 kinds of lines.

vertical	horizontal	circle	slant
|	—	c ɔ o	/ \

Write the words. Pull down straight or push up straight to write vertical lines.

Write the words. Slide left or slide right to write horizontal lines.

tiger elephant deer fish

words. Circle forward or circle backward to write circle lines.

cow goat pig duck

Write the words. Slant left or slant right to write slant lines.

fox lizard wolf skunk

My Own Writing Write a sentence about your favorite animal.

Shape

Circle a word you wrote that has good shape.

Keys to Legibility

Size

Make your writing easy to read.
Look at the size of your letters.

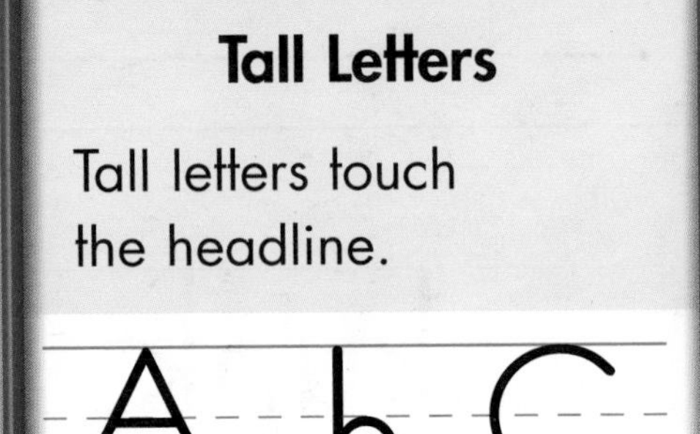

Tall Letters

Tall letters touch the headline.

A b C

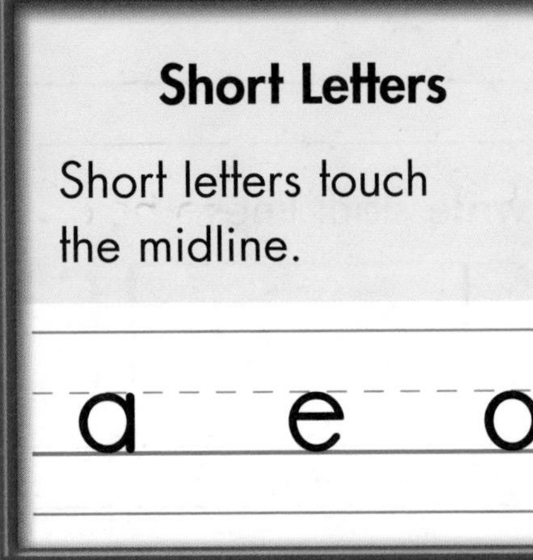

Short Letters

Short letters touch the midline.

a e o

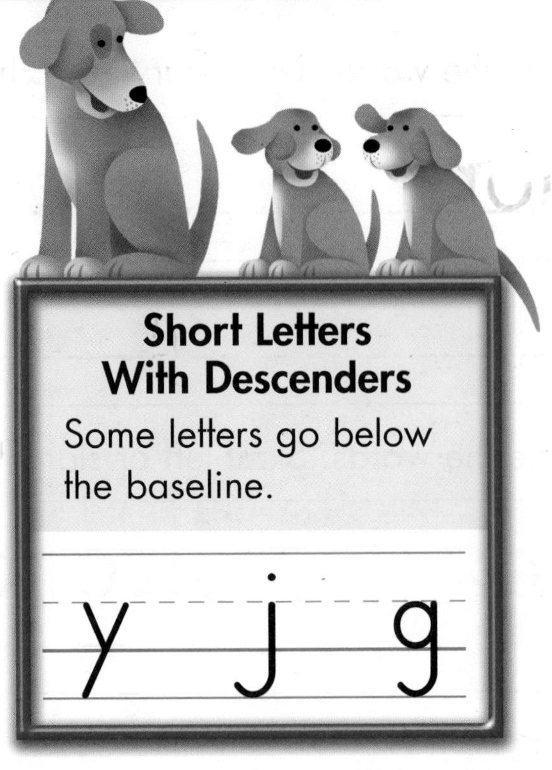

Short Letters With Descenders

Some letters go below the baseline.

y j g

Write the words. Make sure your tall letters touch the headline.

hamster rabbit frog cat

salamander goldfish turtle

Write the words. Make sure your short letters touch the midline.

lion bear mouse zebra

Write the words. Make sure your letters with descenders go below the baseline and touch the next line.

jaguar quail penguin

My Own Writing Write a sentence about a pet you know.

Size

Circle a word you wrote that has good size.

Keys to Legibility

Spacing

Make your writing easy to read. Look at the spacing between letters and words.

PEACH STREET

These letters are too close.

Peach Street

These letters are too far apart.

P e a c h   S t r e e t

Write the street names. Make sure your spacing between letters is just right.

Cherry Lane   Apple Road

Cherry Lane   Apple Road

There should be space for your little finger or a paper clip between words. Write the sentence.

Who lives on Banana Avenue?

Who lives on Banana Avenue?

Find the spacing mistakes in each sentence. Write the sentences correctly.

Sally is going to ride.

Sally is going to ride.

Kam plays o n GrapeRoad.

Kam plays on Grape Road.

Tara lives on P e a r Drive.

Tara lives on Pear Drive.

My Own Writing

Make up a street name. Write about what happens on that street. Use good spacing between your letters and words.

Strawberry Avenue The people of Strawberry Avenue love gardening.

Spacing

Circle a word you wrote that has good spacing.

Keys to Legibility

Slant

Make your writing easy to read.
Look at the slant of your letters.

Here's a good way to check the slant of your letters.
Draw lines through each vertical stroke.

blueberries

If the lines you drew are straight up and down,
your word has good slant.

Write the words. Draw lines to check your slant.

bananas strawberries

bananas strawberries

Write the sentence. Draw lines to check your slant.

I made an apple pie by myself.

I made an apple pie by myself.

These things will help you write with good vertical slant.

1. Position your paper properly.
2. Pull your strokes down in the correct direction.
3. Shift your paper as you write.

Left-Handed Writers

Right-Handed Writers

Write the words correctly. Make sure your writing has good slant.

orange peach pear kiwi

plum apricot grapes

My Own Writing Write a sentence about a fruit you like.

Slant Circle a word you wrote that has good slant.

Only My Opinion

Is a caterpillar ticklish?
Well, it's always my belief
That he giggles as he wiggles
Across a hairy leaf.

Monica Shannon

Unit
2
Writing Numerals

Writing Numerals

Trace and write.

1 1 1 1 1 1

2 2 2 2 2 2

3 3 3 3 3 3

4 4 4 4 4 4

5 5 5 5 5 5

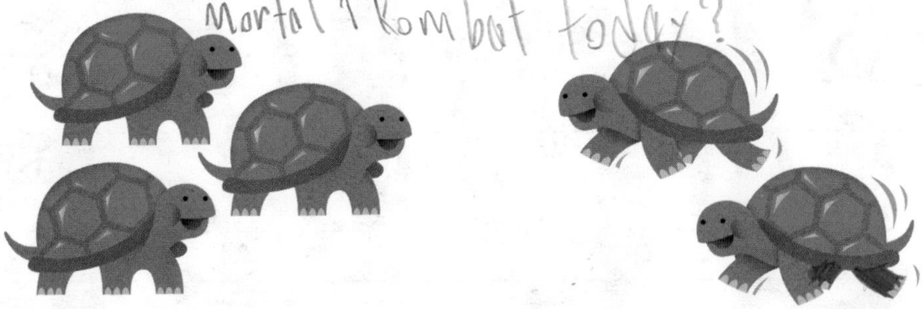

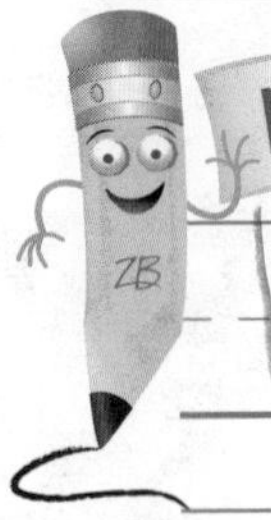

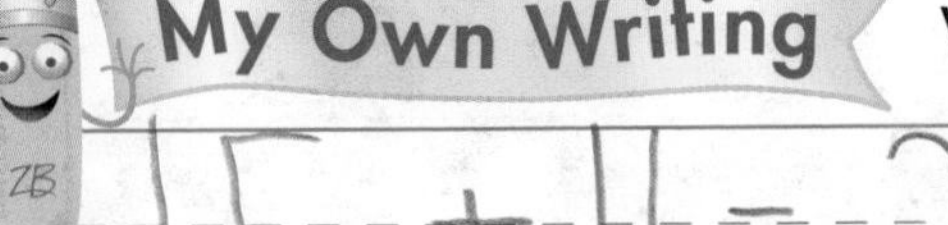

Write a number sentence. Use a plus sign (+).

6 7 8 9 10

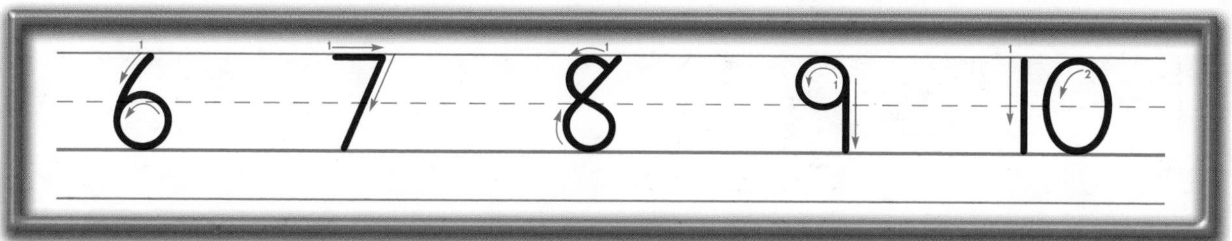

Trace and write.

6 6 6 6 6 6

6 6 6 6 6

7 7 7 7 7 7

7 7 7 7 7

8 8 8 8 8 8

8 8 8 8 8

9 9 9 9 9 9

9 9 9 9 9

10 10 10 10 10

10 10 10 10

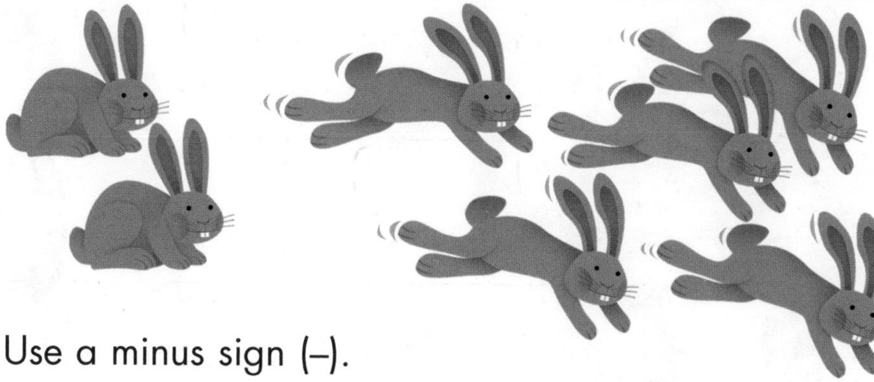

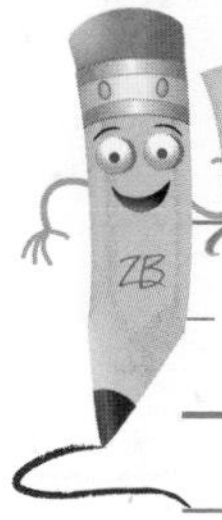

My Own Writing

Write a number sentence. Use a minus sign (–).

26 – 11 = 15

266
268
270
272
6189
51st ST
30
MPH
7340

Write the license number of the blue car.

7340

Write the license number of the red truck.

6189

Write the number of the street.

51st

Write the number that tells how fast to drive.

30

Write the numbers on the doors.

266, 268, 270, 272

My Own Writing Write about something that you see in the picture.

The mom and the kid are waiting to cross the road.

People

Some people talk and talk
and never say a thing.
Some people look at you
and birds begin to sing.

Some people laugh and laugh
and yet you want to cry.
Some people touch your hand
and music fills the sky.

Charlotte Zolotow

Unit 3
Writing Letters and Words

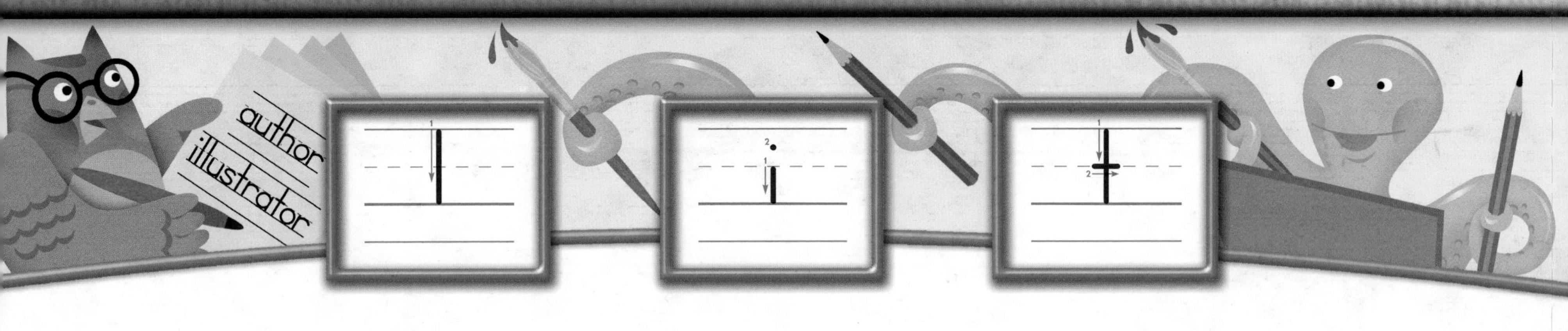

Trace and write.

Stroke descriptions to guide letter formation at home:

1. Pull down straight.

1. Pull down straight. Lift.
2. Dot.

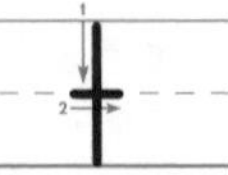

1. Pull down straight. Lift.
2. Slide right.

Stop and Check

Circle your best l.
Circle your best i.
Circle your best t.

Write the words about books.

title author illustrator

title a

fiction nonfiction page

sentence mystery picture

My Own Writing Write a sentence about the kind of books you like.

Shape

Circle your best letter that has a vertical line.

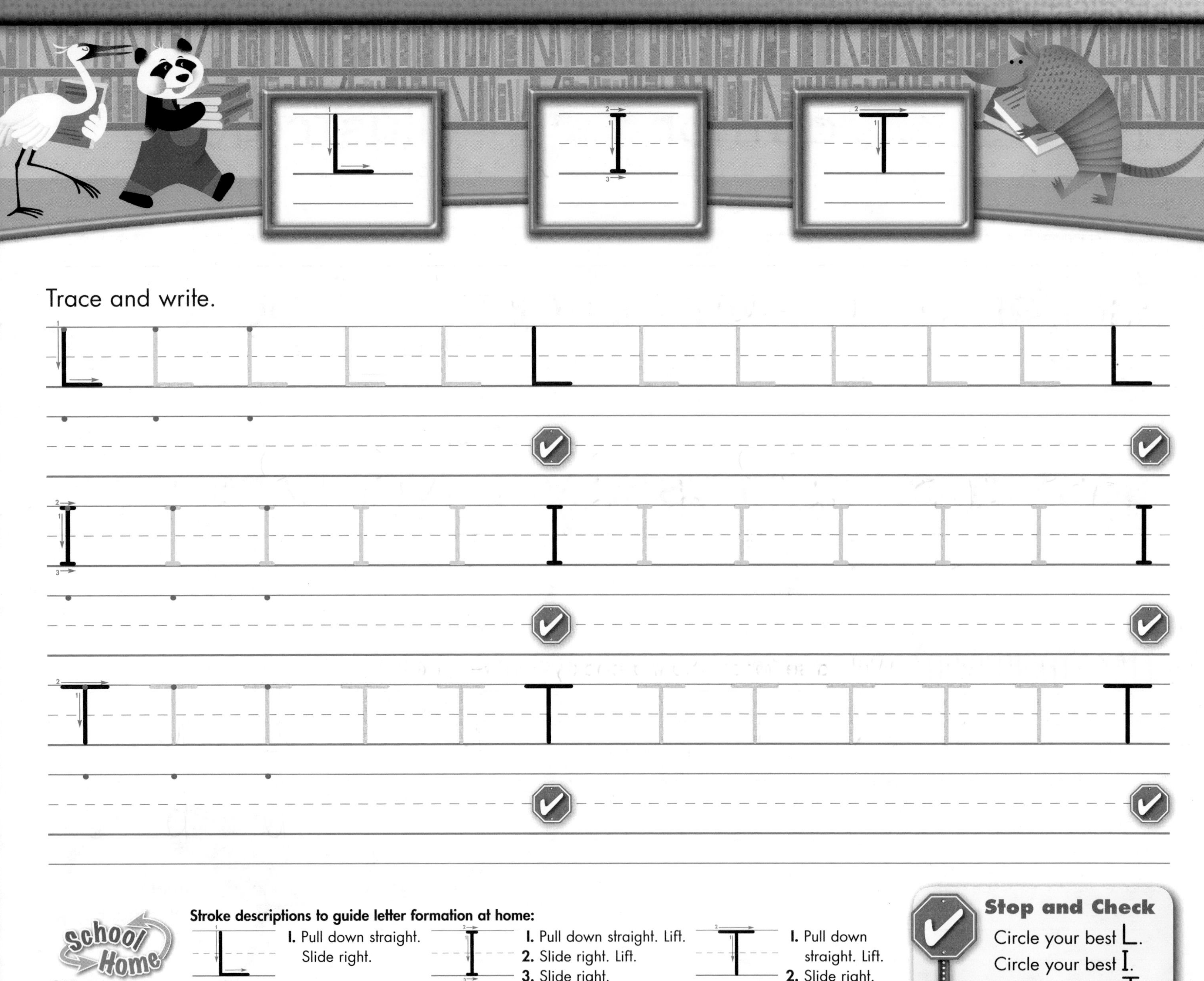

Trace and write.

L L L L L L L L L L L L

I I I I I I I I I I I I

T T T T T T T T T T T T

Stroke descriptions to guide letter formation at home:

School Home

L
1. Pull down straight. Slide right.

I
1. Pull down straight. Lift.
2. Slide right. Lift.
3. Slide right.

T
1. Pull down straight. Lift.
2. Slide right.

Stop and Check

Circle your best L.
Circle your best I.
Circle your best T.

Write the sentences about books.

Let's visit the library.

Let's visit the library.

Is there a book for me?

Is there a book for m?

The man at the desk will help you.

The man at the desk will help you.

My Own Writing Write a sentence about a book you have read.

Percy Jackson is one of the best books I've read.

Size

Circle a word you wrote that has good size.

Trace and write.

o o o o o o o o o o o o

a a a a a a a a a a a a

d d d d d d d d d d d d

Stroke descriptions to guide letter formation at home:

o — **1.** Circle back all the way around.

a — **1.** Circle back all the way around; push up straight. Pull down straight.

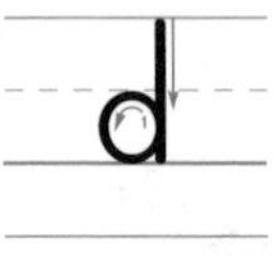

d — **1.** Circle back all the way around; push up straight. Pull down straight.

Stop and Check

Circle your best **o**.
Circle your best **a**.
Circle your best **d**.

Write the words that name landforms.

desert bay island

ocean mountain valley

plain dune canyon

My Own Writing Write a sentence about a landform you have seen.

Spacing

Circle two words with good spacing between them.

Trace and write.

O O O O O O O O O O

A A A A A A A A A A

D D D D D D D D D D

Stroke descriptions to guide letter formation at home:

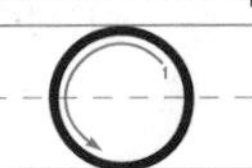

1. Circle back all the way around.

1. Slant left. Lift.
2. Slant right. Lift.
3. Slide right.

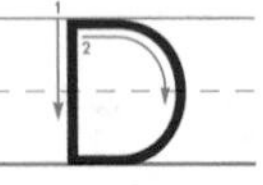

1. Pull down straight. Lift.
2. Slide right; curve forward; slide left.

Stop and Check

Circle your best O.
Circle your best A.
Circle your best D.

Write the sentences about landforms.

Oceans cover part of Earth.

A continent is huge.

Deserts are dry places.

My Own Writing Write a sentence about the continent you live on.

Slant

Circle a letter that is straight up and down.

Review

Ll Ii Tt Oo Aa Dd

Write the list of holidays.

Our Favorite Holidays

Independence Day

Thanksgiving Day

Arbor Day

Labor Day

Write the invitation to a holiday party. Leave space for margins.

It's a Party!

Date: Labor Day
Time: 11:00 A.M.
Place: Olivia's House
Let's all have fun!

Keys to Legibility

Slant
Spacing
Size
Shape

Write the story.
Make your writing easy to read. Be sure to leave space for margins.

The race began. As Ian ran, he felt something odd. His shoe came untied! He knew he must never give up. So one foot was bare

when Ian crossed the finish line.

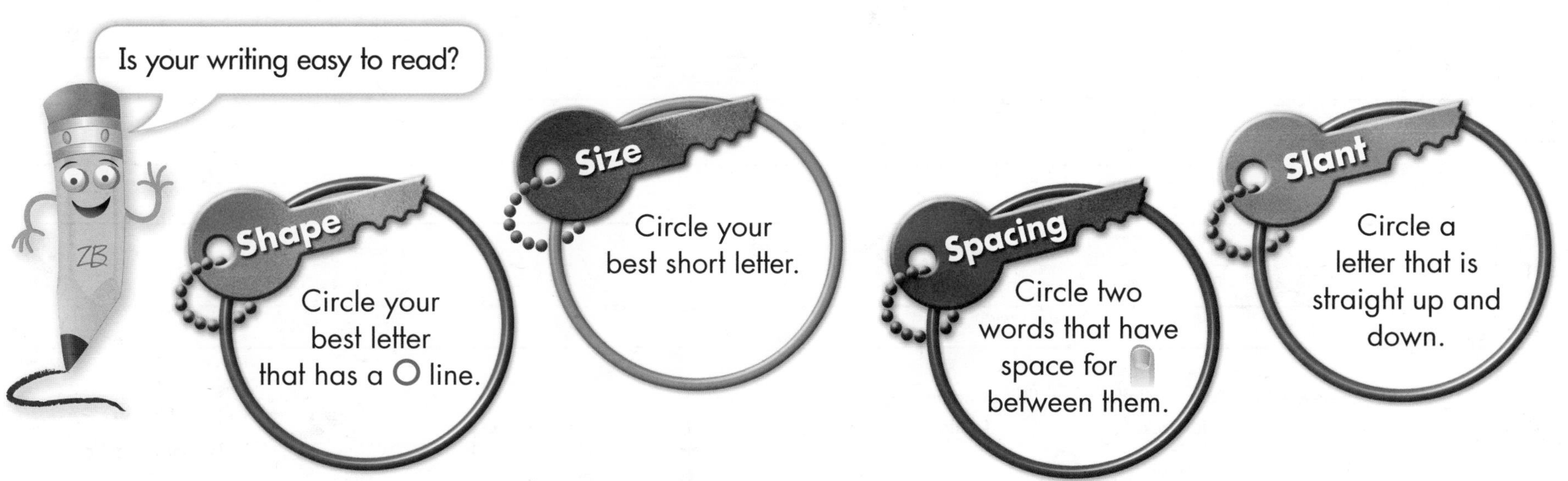

Trace and write.

c c c c c c c c c c c c

e e e e e e e e e e e e

f f f f f f f f f f f f

Stroke descriptions to guide letter formation at home:

c **1.** Circle back.

e **1.** Slide right. Circle back.

f **1.** Curve back; pull down straight. Lift.
2. Slide right.

Stop and Check

Circle your best **c**.

Circle your best **e**.

Circle your best **f**.

Write the words that name breakfast foods.

cereal eggs fruit

cheese bagels waffles

corn muffins juice

My Own Writing Write a sentence about what you eat for breakfast.

Shape

Circle your best letter that has a O line.

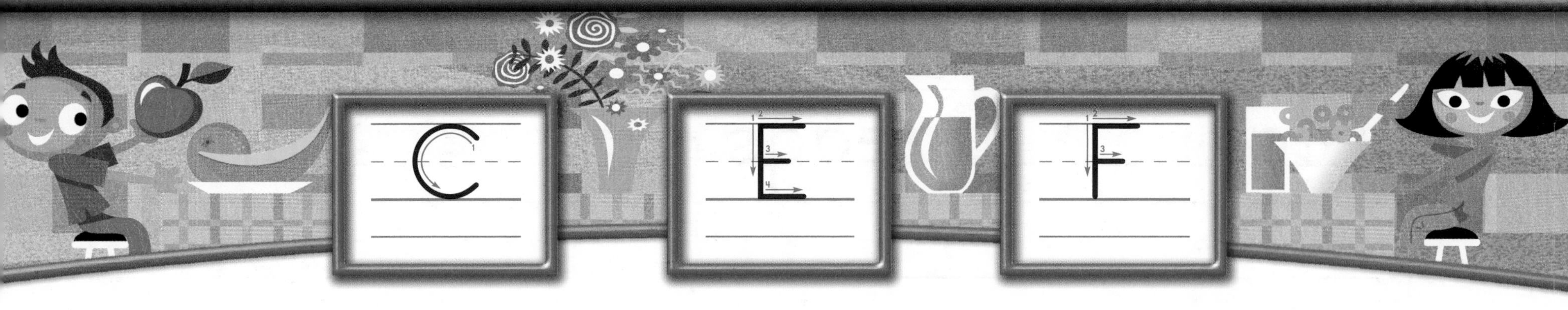

Trace and write.

C C C C C C C C C C C C

E E E E E E E E E E E E

F F F F F F F F F F F F

Stroke descriptions to guide letter formation at home:

C
1. Circle back.

E
1. Pull down straight. Lift.
2. Slide right. Lift.
3. Slide right; stop short. Lift.
4. Slide right.

F
1. Pull down straight. Lift.
2. Slide right. Lift.
3. Slide right; stop short.

Stop and Check

Circle your best C.

Circle your best E.

Circle your best F.

Write the sentences about eating breakfast.

Everyone should eat breakfast.

Food gives your body energy.

Choose good foods to eat.

My Own Writing Write a sentence about your favorite snack.

Trace and write.

g g g g g g g g g g g g

j j j j j j j j j j j j

q q q q q q q q q q q q

Stroke descriptions to guide letter formation at home:

g
1. Circle back all the way around; push up straight. Pull down straight; curve back.

j
1. Pull down straight; curve back. Lift.
2. Dot.

q
1. Circle back all the way around; push up straight. Pull down straight; curve forward.

Stop and Check

Circle your best g.

Circle your best j.

Circle your best q.

Write the words about telling jokes.

jokes question enjoy

giggle squeal laugh

funny quick jolly

My Own Writing

Where can a 3,000-pound elephant sit? Write a sentence to answer the question.

Spacing

Circle two letters with good spacing between them.

Answer: It can sit anywhere it wants.

Trace and write.

G G G G G G G G G G

J J J J J J J J J J

Q Q Q Q Q Q Q Q Q Q

Stroke descriptions to guide letter formation at home:

G 1. Circle back. Slide left.

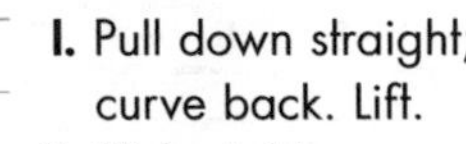

J 1. Pull down straight; curve back. Lift. 2. Slide right.

Q 1. Circle back all the way around. Lift. 2. Slant right.

Stop and Check

Circle your best G.

Circle your best J.

Circle your best Q.

Write the sentences about jokes.

Jokes are such fun to tell.

Gil's joke made me giggle.

Quentin laughed at the joke, too.

My Own Writing Write a sentence about what makes you laugh.

Slant

Circle a word you wrote that is straight up and down.

Review

Cc Ee Ff Gg Jj Qq

Write the names of places.

Mojave Desert Quebec

Eugene, Oregon Georgia

Grand Canyon Jamestown

Ellis Island Petrified Forest

The Grand Canyon

Every year, quite a few visitors come. Just look at the view! Fabulous colors glow like jewels here.

Write the paragraph about the Grand Canyon. Indent the first line of the paragraph. Be sure to leave space for margins.

Stop and Check

Circle a word you wrote that has good size.

Keys to Legibility

Write the directions to a friend's house.
Make your writing easy to read, leaving space for margins.

Follow Dodd Lane through town.

Turn left at a round green bush.

Before the end of the road,

try to get in the right lane.

At the fork in the road, go right.

Trace and write.

u u u u u u u u u u u u

s s s s s s s s s s s s

Stroke descriptions to guide letter formation at home:

u
1. Pull down straight; curve forward; push up. Pull down straight.

s
1. Curve back; curve forward.

Stop and Check

Circle your best **u**.

Circle your best **s**.

Write the words about sea life.

seaweed fish sea horse

tiger shark underwater

turtle swim octopus

My Own Writing Write a sentence about something that lives in the ocean.

Trace and write.

U U U U U U U U U U U U

S S S S S S S S S S S S

Stroke descriptions to guide letter formation at home:

U **1.** Pull down straight; curve forward; push up.

1. Curve back; curve forward.

Stop and Check

Circle your best U.

Circle your best S.

Write the facts about seals.

Seals can swim very fast.

Usually, seals eat fish.

Seals make a sound like a horn.

My Own Writing Write a sentence about a sea animal you like.

Trace and write.

b b b b b b b b b b b b

p p p p p p p p p p p p

r r r r r r r r r r r r

Stroke descriptions to guide letter formation at home:

1. Pull down straight. Push up; circle forward.

p

1. Pull down straight. Push up; circle forward.

1. Pull down straight. Push up; curve forward.

Stop and Check

Circle your best b.

Circle your best p.

Circle your best r.

Write the words that name things found near a pond.

bugs chipmunk bridge

rabbit frogs tadpoles

beaver reeds raccoon

My Own Writing Write a sentence about an animal that lives near a pond.

Spacing

Circle two words with good spacing between them.

Trace and write.

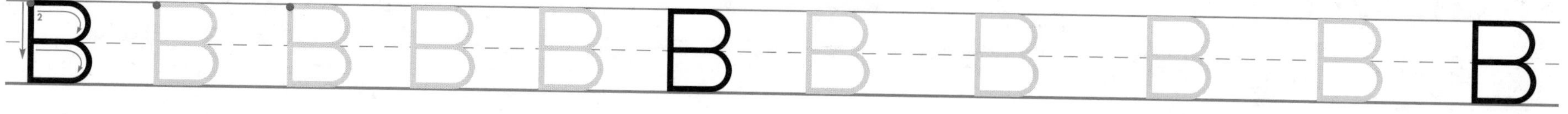

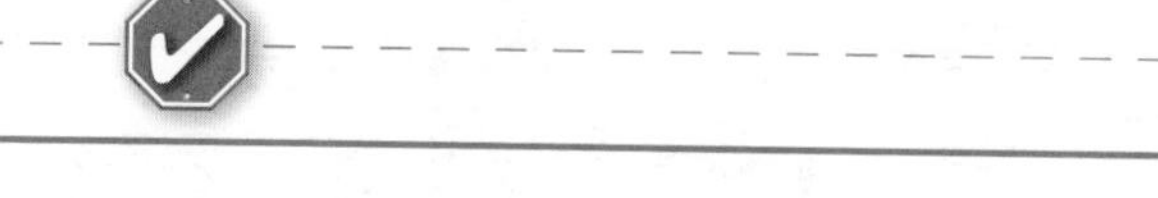

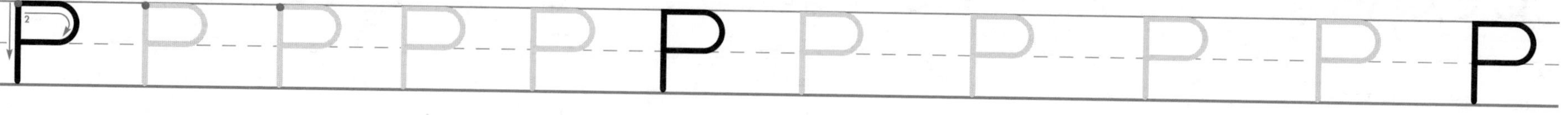

Stroke descriptions to guide letter formation at home:

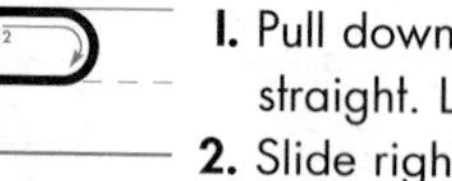

B
1. Pull down straight. Lift.
2. Slide right; curve forward; slide left. Slide right; curve forward; slide left.

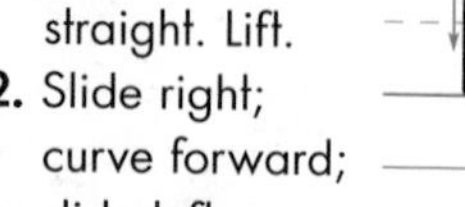

P
1. Pull down straight. Lift.
2. Slide right; curve forward; slide left.

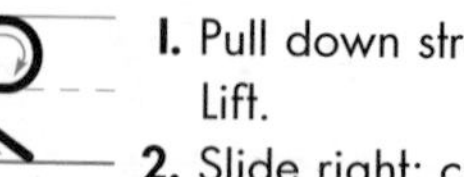

R
1. Pull down straight. Lift.
2. Slide right; curve forward; slide left. Slant right.

Stop and Check

Circle your best B.

Circle your best P.

Circle your best R.

Write the sentences about pond life.

Reeds grow near the pond.

Busy beavers build dams.

Ponds are full of life!

My Own Writing Write a sentence about something that might happen by a pond.

Slant

Circle a word that is straight up and down.

Trace and write.

n n n n n n n n n n n n

m m m m m m m m m m m m

h h h h h h h h h h h h

Stroke descriptions to guide letter formation at home:

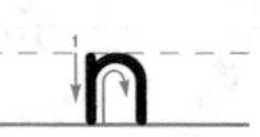

1. Pull down straight. Push up; curve forward; pull down straight.

1. Pull down straight. Push up; curve forward; pull down straight. Push up; curve forward; pull down straight.

1. Pull down straight. Push up; curve forward; pull down straight.

Stop and Check

Circle your best **n**.

Circle your best **m**.

Circle your best **h**.

Write the words about math.

count half money

measure tens many

even number hundreds

My Own Writing Write a sentence about a way that you use numbers.

Shape

Circle your best letter that has a / line.

Trace and write.

N N N N N N N N N N

M M M M M M M M M M

H H H H H H H H H H

Stroke descriptions to guide letter formation at home:

N
1. Pull down straight.
Lift.
2. Slant right.
Push up straight.

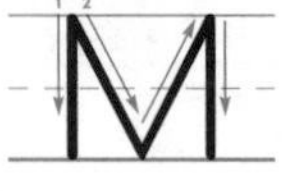

M
1. Pull down straight.
Lift.
2. Slant right.
Slant up.
Pull down straight.

H
1. Pull down straight.
Lift.
2. Pull down straight.
Lift.
3. Slide right.

Stop and Check

Circle your best N.
Circle your best M.
Circle your best H.

Write the sentences about the number nine.

My favorite numeral is nine.

Nine plus one. What is the sum?

How many threes equal nine?

My Own Writing What is your favorite number? Write a sentence that tells why it is your favorite.

Size

Circle a word you wrote that has good size.

Uu Ss Bb Pp Rr Nn Mm Hh

Write the book titles. Remember to underline.

Madeline's Rescue

Babar Saves the Day

Teach Us, Amelia Bedelia

The Napping House

Teach Us, Amelia Bedelia

A character named Amelia Bedelia went to school one day. She got everything mixed up. I like her.

Write the sentences about the funny book. Leave space for margins.

Stop and Check

Circle a word you wrote that has good spacing.

Keys to Legibility

Slant
Spacing
Size
Shape

Write the business letter.
Leave space for margins.
Make your writing easy to read.

Dear Mr. and Mrs. Brown,

Do you need help on your farm?

I think I am a good farmhand.

Yours truly,

Marcus Spencer

Trace and write.

v v v v v v v v v v v v

y y y y y y y y y y y y

w w w w w w w w w w w w

Stroke descriptions to guide letter formation at home:

v — **1.** Slant right. Slant up.

y — **1.** Slant right. Lift.
2. Slant left.

w — **1.** Slant right. Slant up.
Slant right. Slant up.

Stop and Check

Circle your best **v**.

Circle your best **y**.

Circle your best **w**.

Write the words about weather.

vapor warm above

snowy cloudy rainy

windy sunny twister

My Own Writing Write a sentence about today's weather.

Spacing

Circle two letters with good spacing between them.

Trace and write.

V V V V V V V V V V

Y Y Y Y Y Y Y Y Y Y

W W W W W W W W

Stroke descriptions to guide letter formation at home:

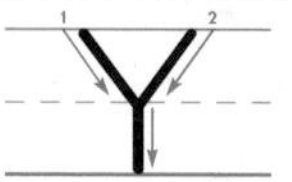

I. Slant right. Slant up.

I. Slant right. Lift.
2. Slant left. Pull down straight.

W

I. Slant right. Slant up. Slant right. Slant up.

Stop and Check

Circle your best V.

Circle your best Y.

Circle your best W.

Write the sentences about a windy day.

Windy days can be nice.

Oh boy! Your kite can fly high!

Val's kite can soar like a plane.

My Own Writing Write a sentence about your favorite kind of weather.

Slant

Circle a letter you wrote that is straight up and down.

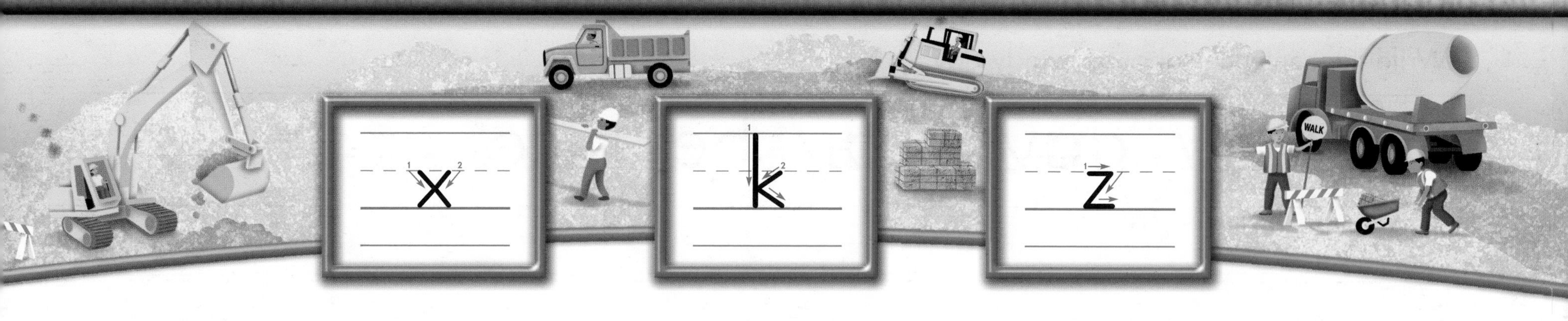

Trace and write.

x x x x x x x x x x x x

k k k k k k k k k k k k

z z z z z z z z z z z z

Stroke descriptions to guide letter formation at home:

x
1. Slant right. Lift.
2. Slant left.

1. Pull down straight. Lift.
2. Slant left. Slant right.

z
1. Slide right.
Slant left.
Slide right.

Stop and Check

Circle your best **x**.

Circle your best **k**.

Circle your best **z**.

Write the words about building.

cement mixer bricks

dump truck work zone

bulldozer backhoe

My Own Writing Write a sentence about something you would like to build.

Shape

Circle your best letter that has a l line.

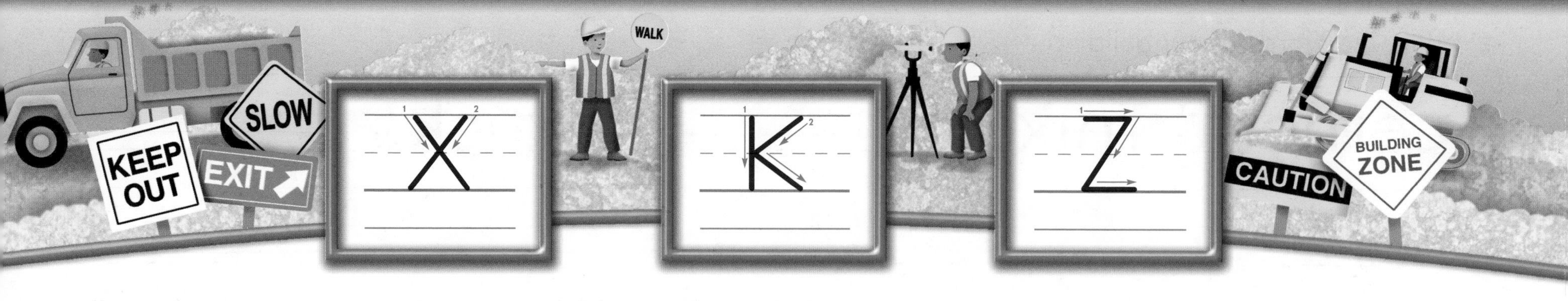

Trace and write.

X X X X X X X X X X

K K K K K K K K K K

Z Z Z Z Z Z Z Z Z Z

Stroke descriptions to guide letter formation at home:

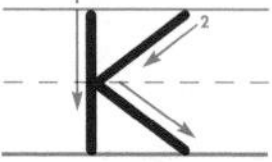
1. Slant right. Lift.
2. Slant left.

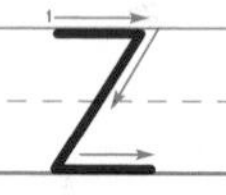
1. Pull down straight. Lift.
2. Slant left. Slant right.

Z
1. Slide right.
Slant left.
Slide right.

Stop and Check

Circle your best X.
Circle your best K.
Circle your best Z.

Write the words found on the signs.

Building Zone Keep Out

EXIT Caution

Slow WALK

My Own Writing Write words from other signs you have seen.

Write the state names and abbreviations.

NV Nevada WY Wyoming

TX Texas AR Arkansas

AZ Arizona WI Wisconsin

Application

Today is Wednesday. We drove all day. I saw TX or NV on many license plates. I know TX stands for Texas. NV must mean Nevada.

Write the travel journal. Indent the first line of the paragraph. Be sure to leave space for margins.

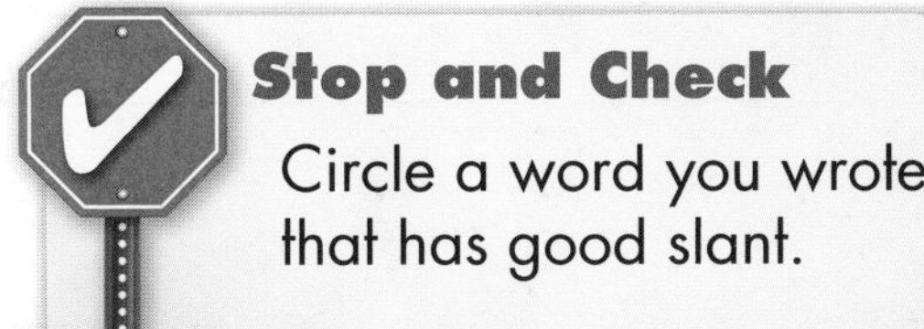

Stop and Check

Circle a word you wrote that has good slant.

Keys to Legibility

Slant
Spacing
Size
Shape

Write the personal narrative.
Make your writing easy to read. Be sure to leave space for margins.

I went to town with my mother.

We rode an old train.

It was very crowded.

Two men gave us their seats.

"How kind," my mother said.

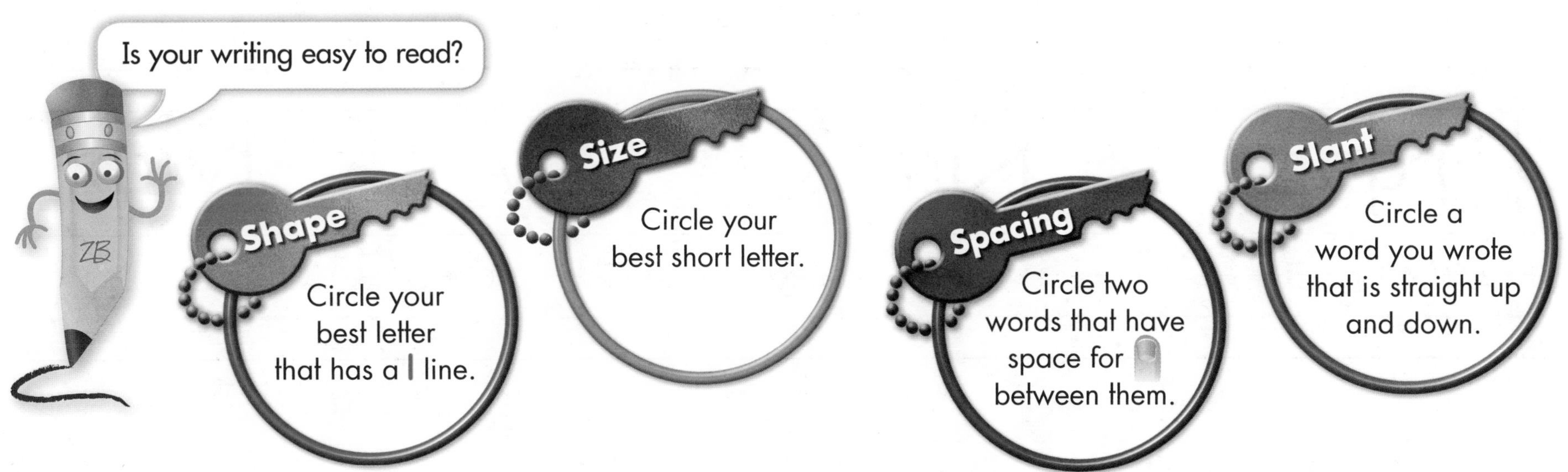

Write the name for each letter of the alphabet.

Azize Bobby Connor

Dionne Elijah Felipe

Greg Howard Isabel

Jordan Kim Lily Max

Noah Olivia Pasqual

Quintana Rick Sofia

Terry Ursula Victor

Wan Xavier Yolanda

Zuria

My writing has good Shape.

My writing has good Size.

My writing has good Spacing.

My writing has good Slant.

Number Fun

Fill in the missing dates on the calendar.

MARCH

Sunday	Monday	Tuesday	Wednesday	Thursday	Friday	Saturday
	1	2				
	8		10	11	12 soccer game	13
14	15		17	18	19 No School	20
21		23 Emily's birthday		25 picnic at White Rock Lake		27
		30	31 class play			

Look at the calendar. Then write sentences to answer the questions.

1. On what date is the class play?

2. On what date is the picnic at White Rock Lake?

3. What will happen on March 12?

4. On what date is Emily's birthday?

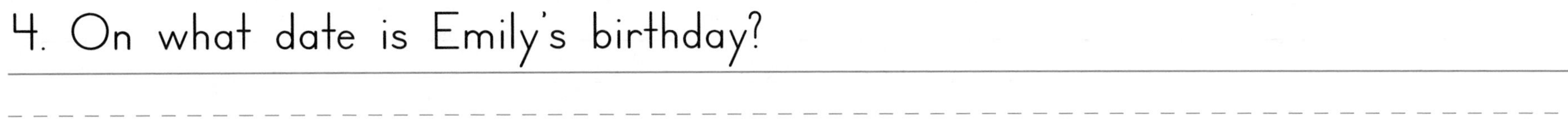

Visit Number Land

Write the addresses for five of the houses you see.

Choose one house from the picture. Write the address of the house. Tell about who might live there. Leave space for margins.

STONE ST

LAKE AVE

Slant

Circle a numeral you wrote that is straight up and down.

Show What You Can Do

Write the title and the first four lines of the poem in your best handwriting. Be sure to leave space for margins.

In the evening the city
Goes to bed
Hanging lights
About its head.
by Langston Hughes

Write the next four lines here. Leave space for margins.

The Purple Cow

I never saw a purple cow,
I never hope to see one;
But I can tell you, anyhow,
I'd rather see than be one.

Gelett Burgess

Unit 4
Using What You Have Learned

Why Do You Write?

On the following pages, you will write about many interesting things. You will write for many reasons. Thinking about Shape, Size, Spacing, and Slant will help you make your writing easy to read. Read to find out why these students are writing.

My Own Writing Write a sentence about something you have written.

Let's Get Ready to Write

Before you write, think about your topic.
Make a list of ideas for your story.

Here are some ideas for a story about a fox.
Write words that tell what the fox is like and what it does.

Describing Words

red
small
quick
daring
smart

Action Words

runs
jumps
looks
hides
eats

Choose an animal to write about. Draw a picture in the box.
Then write words that tell what the animal is like and what it does.

Shape

Circle three words you wrote that have good shape.

Making a Web

Write the words to complete the Web.

call Grandpa

read

feed self

finish picture

clean up

study spelling

Complete this Web by writing things you need to do.

My Things to Do

Size

Circle three words you wrote that have good size.

It's So Cold!

Write the names of things to wear or do when it is cold outside.

Write a story about a snowy day. Be sure to indent the first line and leave space for margins.

Spacing

Circle a word you wrote that has good spacing.

It's So Warm!

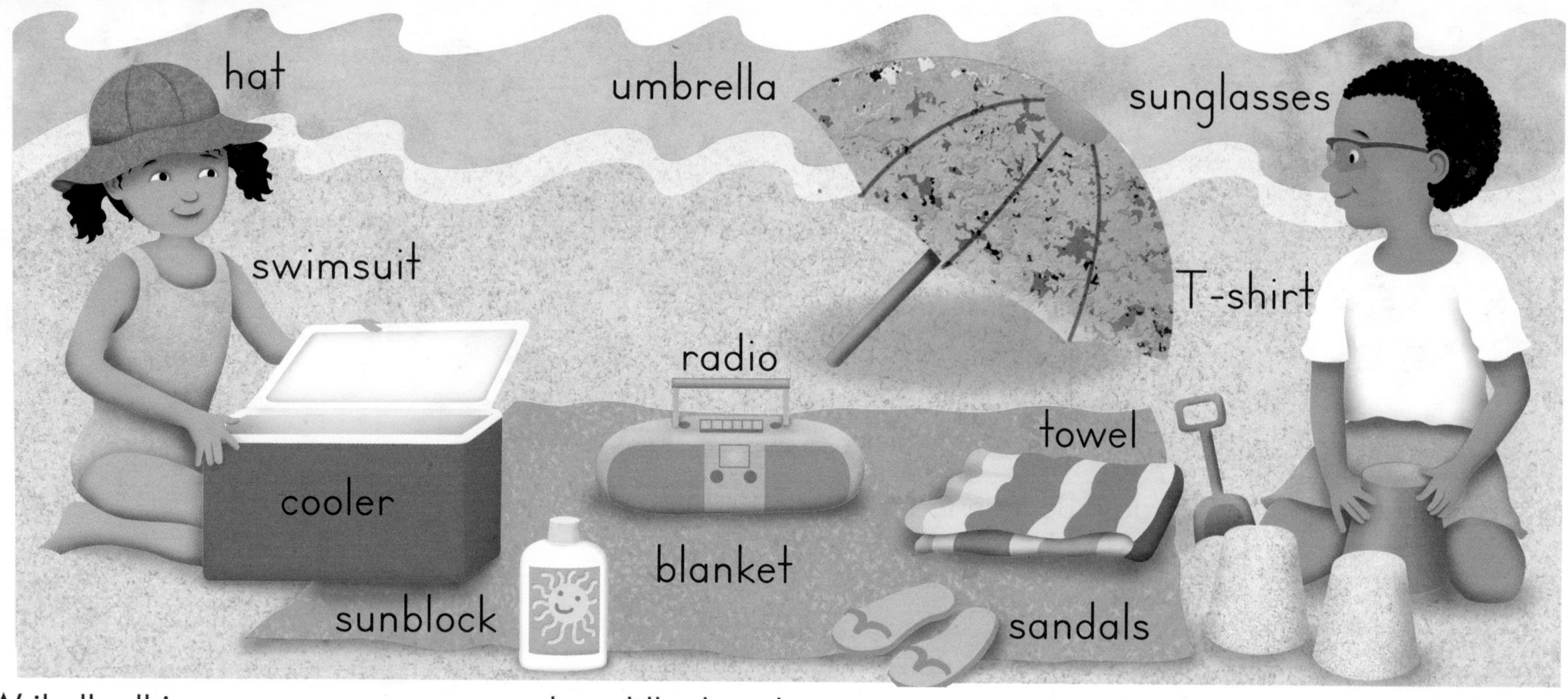

Write the things you see on a warm day at the beach.

Write a story about what you like to do when the weather is warm. Be sure to leave space for margins.

Slant

Circle three words you wrote that have good slant.

Computer Chat

screen
e-mail
mouse
keyboard
online
mousepad
click
print
World Wide Web

Write the words about computers.

Write an e-mail to a friend. Be sure to leave space for margins.

Shape

Circle three words you wrote that have good shape.

Tasting Time

Sweet	Sour	Salty	Spicy
strawberries	lemons	pretzels	salsa
watermelons	pickles	peanuts	mustard
cherries	grapefruits	chips	chili
bananas	limes	crackers	peppers

Choose two of the lists.
Write one list here.

Write another list here.

Write about your favorite meal. Describe how the food looks and tastes. Be sure to leave space for margins.

Size

Circle a word you wrote that has good size.

Helping Hands

share your supplies

put books away

help teacher

take turns

clean up

pass out papers

Write things you can do to help at school.
Use the words above or add other ideas.

Write a list of ways to help at home. Be sure to leave space for margins.

Ways to Help at Home:

Spacing

Circle three words you wrote that have good spacing.

I Can Do It!

Here are some easy steps to follow to make a healthy sandwich.

You will need:

two slices of bread

cheese

sliced tomatoes

lettuce leaves

1. Put cheese on a slice of bread.
2. Cover cheese with tomato.
3. Also cover with lettuce.
4. Cover with other slice of bread.
5. Enjoy!

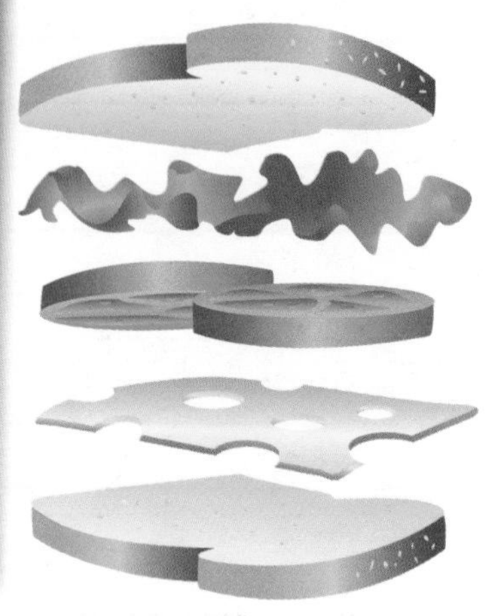

Write the steps to follow when making a cheese, lettuce, and tomato sandwich.

Think of a food you can make. Write the steps to follow when making it. Leave space for margins.

Slant

Circle a word you wrote that has good slant.

In a Night Sky

Write the names of things you see in a night sky.

Look at the picture of the moon.
Write sentences to tell what you know about the moon.

Writing Quickly

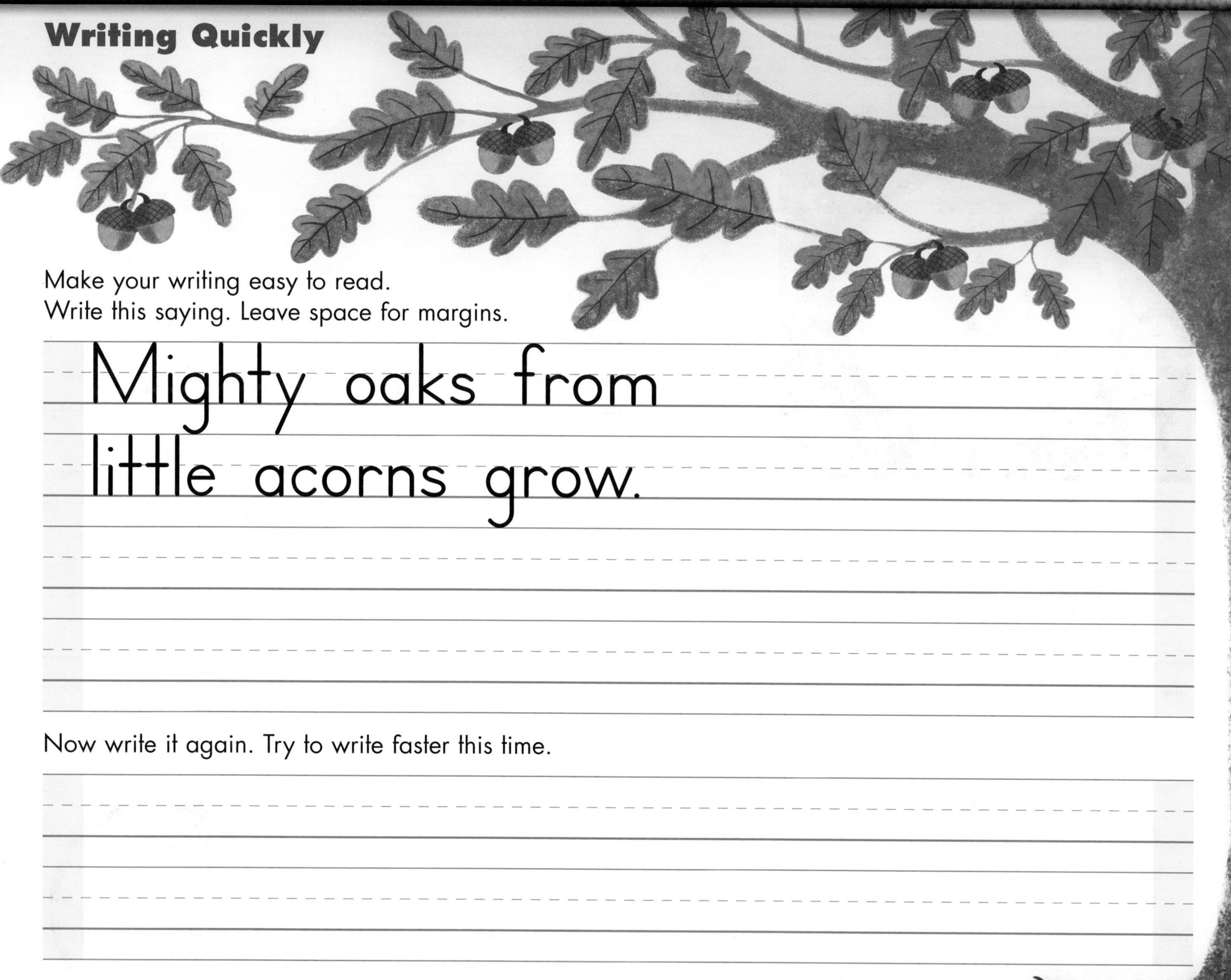

Make your writing easy to read.
Write this saying. Leave space for margins.

Mighty oaks from
little acorns grow.

Now write it again. Try to write faster this time.

Write the saying again. Try to write even faster.
Make sure your writing is easy to read.

Now read your writing. Ask others to read it, too.
Then circle Yes or No next to each sentence.

My writing is easy for me to read.	Yes	No
My writing is easy for others to read.	Yes	No

Writing Easily

When your writing flows easily, you don't have to worry about your handwriting. You can just think about what you want to say.

Read the writing prompt below. Write your story on the lines. Let your handwriting flow easily.

Narrative Writing

Write a story about what you see in the picture. Tell what might happen next.

Now read your final writing. Circle Yes or No to respond to each statement. Then show your writing to another reader, either a classmate or your teacher. Ask that person to circle Yes or No beside each statement.

	My Evaluation	My Classmate's or Teacher's Evaluation
The writing is easy to read.	Yes No	Yes No
The writing has good Shape.	Yes No	Yes No
The writing has good Size.	Yes No	Yes No
The writing has good Spacing.	Yes No	Yes No
The writing has good Slant.	Yes No	Yes No

Handwriting and the Writing Process

Write about a special place you visited. Tell what you saw there. Write on a piece of writing paper. Follow these five steps as you write.

1. Prewriting

Plan ideas for your writing.
Use good handwriting
so you can read your ideas later.

2. Drafting

Write your ideas in sentences.
Your writing should be easy to read.

3. Revising

Revise your writing.
Make changes so that it says what you mean.

4. Editing

Check your spelling, punctuation, and handwriting.
Make sure your writing is easy to read.

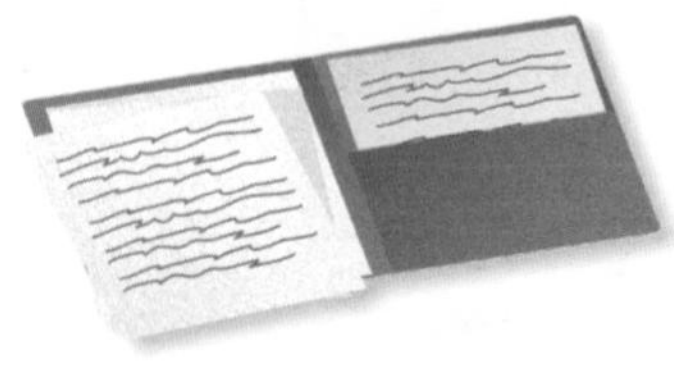

5. Publishing

Share your writing with others.
Use your best handwriting.

Record of Student's Handwriting Skills

Manuscript

	Needs Improvement	Shows Mastery
Uses good sitting position	☐	☐
Positions paper correctly	☐	☐
Holds pencil correctly	☐	☐
Writes vertical lines	☐	☐
Writes horizontal lines	☐	☐
Writes circle lines	☐	☐
Writes slant lines	☐	☐
Writes numerals **1–10**	☐	☐
Writes **l, i, t**	☐	☐
Writes **L, I, T**	☐	☐
Writes **o, a, d**	☐	☐
Writes **O, A, D**	☐	☐
Writes **c, e, f**	☐	☐
Writes **C, E, F**	☐	☐
Writes **g, j, q**	☐	☐
Writes **G, J, Q**	☐	☐

	Needs Improvement	Shows Mastery
Writes **u, s**	☐	☐
Writes **U, S**	☐	☐
Writes **b, p, r**	☐	☐
Writes **B, P, R**	☐	☐
Writes **n, m, h**	☐	☐
Writes **N, M, H**	☐	☐
Writes **v, y, w**	☐	☐
Writes **V, Y, W**	☐	☐
Writes **x, k, z**	☐	☐
Writes **X, K, Z**	☐	☐
Writes with correct shape	☐	☐
Writes with correct size	☐	☐
Writes with correct spacing	☐	☐
Writes with correct slant	☐	☐
Regularly checks written work for legibility	☐	☐

Index